GRADE **3** THR

POWERTHINK

Cooperative Critical Thinking Activities

Written by Anita Reith Stohs

Illustrated by Becky J. Radtke

Editor: Hanna Otero

Cover Design: Kristin Lock

Graphic Artists: Danielle Dela Cruz and Anthony Strasburger

FS112112 POWERTHINK–Grade Three
All rights reserved-Printed in the U.S.A.
Copyright ©2000 Frank Schaffer Publications
23740 Hawthorne Blvd., Torrance, CA 90505

Table of Contents

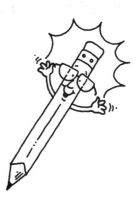

"There are one-story intellects, two-story intellects and three-story intellects with skylights. All fact collectors who have no aim beyond their facts are one-story people. Two-story people compare, reason, generalize, using the labor of the fact collectors as their own. Three-story people idealize, imagine, predict – their best illumination comes from above through the skylight."

Oliver Wendell Holmes

As educators, our goal is to assist students to become "third-story thinkers." Both the National Council of Teachers of Mathematics and the National Science Teachers Association recommend including problem solving and decision making as major goals of education.

What is critical thinking? Research indicates that the skill most basic to critical thinking is the ability to listen or read actively while continuously analyzing the information being presented. Sounds pretty basic, doesn't it? This ability requires the learner to be able to engage in an internal dialogue. Effective learners can dialogue internally without skipping steps.

Current recommendations suggest that children can best learn critical thinking skills by working in small groups or pairs. Working in pairs forces students to externalize their thinking – to think aloud, and to identify errors and skipped steps. It also teaches students to recognize and edit unsystematic thinking in themselves and others.

The **POWERTHINK** series of reproducible activity sheets is designed to provide cooperative learning opportunities for either small groups or pairs. There are six levels of challenge in the **POWERTHINK** series, allowing you to introduce critical thinking material at a sequential pace.

This **POWERTHINK** book provides you with activity sheets that pertain to the major content areas of language arts, social studies, mathematics, science, art, and problem solving.

Levels 1, 2, and 3 of the **POWERTHINK** series are designed clearly and simply:

The Power Play symbol indicates the directions to the students. The icon shows two students working together, but small groups of three will work in many cases.

The Lightning Strike icon indicates extended activities to guide your students to further observations or academic destinations.

Under the dashed line on each activity sheet you will find the Power Up icon. These are the author's comments and directions to the educator on how to prepare the children for the activity. When you're ready to make copies of the activity sheets for your students, simply fold back on the dashed lines and this section will not appear on your student copies.

The teaching of critical thinking skills can also be a forum for truly individual positive reinforcement, so on page 63 you will find a list of powerful verbal reinforcers. Use these to encourage your students to become **"POWERTHINKERS."**

Happy **POWERTHINKING!**

DESK TOOLS

 ## Power Play

1. Here are some items you and your partner might have in your desks. What else can you add?

Paper

_____

Pen

_____

Pencil

_____

Book

_____

Scissors

_____

Stapler

_____

Ruler

_____

_____ _____

_____ _____

_____ _____

2. Look over your list. Many of the things you use are used by workers to do their jobs. Work together to write down how a worker might use each item on your list.

 ## Lightning Strike!

Take turns naming things in your desk or classroom that you use to do your school work. Explain how they could be used by a worker on the job.

 ## Power Up!

Students need to learn to transfer information to new settings. This exercise helps them see how the school supplies they work with every day are also used by adults in grown-up jobs.

• Have the children identify things on your desk that are the same as items in their desks. Explain that adults in many other jobs use the same things students use to do their work.

RECIPE TIME

Power Play

A recipe has two kinds of information:
1. What you need
2. What you do

Write a recipe for use at a class party. Have one person write what you need and the other write what you do to make the recipe. Together, think of a name for your recipe.

Recipe Name _____

What you need:

_____   _____

_____   _____

_____   _____

_____   _____

What you do:

_____

_____

_____

_____

_____

Lightning Strike!

Plan a meal for your family and write a recipe for each part of it.

Power Up!

Students can see how basic guidelines are applied to different situations as they use guidelines for writing a recipe to create their own recipe.

- Show an example of a recipe card that contains both the ingredients needed and the directions for their use.

FOUR IN A ROW

Power Play

Look at the categories at the top of the squares. Look at the letters at the side of the squares. Work with a partner to fill in each square with a word that fits into the category and starts with the same letter.

	Place	Animal	Clothing	Person's Name
B				
P				
S				
D				

Lightning Strike!

1. Use your ruler to draw another playing card. Take turns writing your own categories and letters beside the squares. Fill them in with a partner.
2. Draw a playing card with a different number of squares: Use three or five in a row.
3. Play "Four in a Row" with another group in your class.

Power Up!

Students show their understanding of a given area of knowledge by being able to give examples of things that illustrate that category.

- Explain how to fill in the squares above with words in each category that start with the letters given down the sides of the squares.

ON YOUR TOES

Power Play

1. To **compare** two objects means to look at ways they are alike. How is a balloon like a ball? Both are round. Both bounce. Both are toys.
2. Work with a partner. Think of two more ways they are alike. Write them below.

   Both _____

   Both _____

3. Compare a shoe and a sock. Talk with your partner about how a shoe and a sock are alike. Think of as many ways as you can. Write your ideas below.

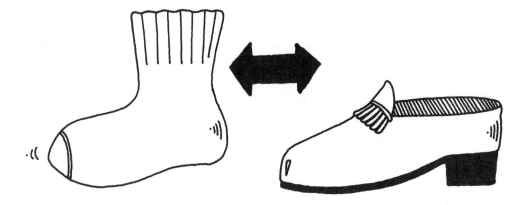

Both are worn on your feet.

   Both _____

   Both _____

   Both _____

   Both _____

Lightning Strike!

Compare other objects that seem very different. How are a horse and an airplane alike? How about a hippopotamus and a mouse?

- -

Power Up!

By comparing objects that seem dissimilar at first, students learn to look at both objects in new ways.
- Ask a student to name two dissimilar objects. Have the class brainstorm to find ways they are similar.

PUTTING IT TOGETHER

Power Play

1. Look at the objects in the box.
2. Talk with your partner about which of these objects are alike. For example: a flower is like a tree because they both need sunshine to grow.
3. Write the name of the object below the group name. You can put an object in more than one group.

Soft objects

Living things

Round objects

Lightning Strike!

Write the names of other objects that fit into more than one of the categories listed. What other group names could you use that fit two or more of the objects shown in the box?

Power Up!

This activity provides students with the chance to experiment with different ways to categorize and label objects. They can see how an object can fit into more than one category.

- Gather several objects together from your desk. Have students suggest different ways to categorize them.

Name(s)_____

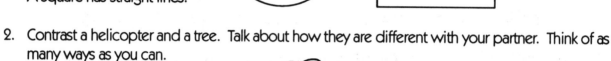

TREES CAN'T FLY

Power Play

1. To **contrast** means to look at ways things are different. Think about a square and a circle. How are they different?

   A circle is round.
   A square is not round.

   A circle has no straight lines.
   A square has straight lines.

2. Contrast a helicopter and a tree. Talk about how they are different with your partner. Think of as many ways as you can.

   Trees can't fly.
   Helicopters don't grow.

3. Write your ideas below.

_____

_____

_____

_____

_____

_____

Lightning Strike!

Contrast two items that seem much the same, like a dog and a cat or a car and a truck. Now compare the same two items and look for ways they are alike.

- -

Power Up!

By contrasting objects, students learn to look at differences that may not be apparent at first. Ask a student to name two similar objects. Have the class brainstorm to find ways they are different.

Frank Schaffer Publications   FS112112 POWERTHINK

MAKE THE CONNECTION

Power Play
Take turns with your partner reading the sentences and writing the answers.

1. **Hole** is to **snake** as **nest** is to _____.

2. **Puppy** is to **dog** as **kitten** is to _____.

3. **Glove** is to **hand** as **sock** is to _____.

4. **Whale** is to **water** as **elephant** is to _____.

5. **Sheep** is to **wool** as **chicken** is to _____.

6. **Spots** are to **leopards** as **stripes** are to _____.

7. **Tadpole** is to **frog** as **caterpillar** is to _____.

8. **Scales** are to **snakes** as **feathers** are to _____.

9. **Hour** is to **day** as **month** is to _____.

10. **Talk** is to **telephone** as **read** is to _____.

Lightning Strike!
Make up other riddles for your partner to solve.

- -

Power Up!
Students need to grow in their ability to see the connection between different objects. This exercise gives them practice in thinking through the connection between similar objects.
- Write the following on the board and have the students fill in the final blank:
  Shoe is to **foot** as **hat** is to _____ (head).

WHAT IF?

Power Play

1. What if you were suddenly only six inches (15 cm) tall? How would that change the way you would use these objects? Work with your partner and think of new uses for the following items.

Eraser _____

Crayon _____

Scissors_____

Tissue _____

2. What other things could you use in a different way?

Object	**Use**
_____	_____
_____	_____
_____	_____
_____	_____
_____	_____

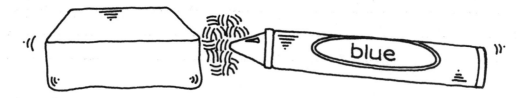

Lightning Strike!

What if, instead of getting smaller, you got bigger? What things would you have to use in a new way?

Power Up!

Students speculate on how common objects would have a different use if the students were a different size.

• Hold up an object from your desk and have the students tell how it could be used if they were only six inches (15 cm) tall.

IN THE BAG

Power Play

1. **POWERTHINKERS** look at objects in new ways. They ask questions and come up with new ideas.
2. What could you do with a brown paper grocery bag? You could fill it with groceries or other objects. You could use the paper to wrap a package.
3. What other uses can you think of for a paper grocery bag? Work with your partner. Talk about ideas. Try to think of the grocery bag in new ways. Write your ideas below.

Lightning Strike!

1. Read your two best ideas to the class. Listen to other people's ideas. Were you surprised at all the good ideas?
2. Look at other objects and see how many new ways you can think of to use them.

Power Up!

To develop critical thinking skills, students need to look at familiar objects in new ways.

- Encourage students to think of other uses for common objects like a brick, a cardboard box, a paper clip, and a tennis ball.

13

FS112112 POWERTHINK · Frank Schaffer Publications

FINISH THE PATTERN

Power Play

1. With a partner, take turns completing the following patterns.

○ △ □ ○ △ □ ○ ___ ___ ___

○ △ ○ ○ □ ○ △ ___ ___ ___

○ ○ △ ○ ○ □ ○ ○ △ ○ ___ ___ ___

○ △ ○ □ ○ ○ ○ ○ △ ○ □ ___ ___ ___

2. Take turns using these shapes to make patterns for your partner to complete.

Lightning Strike!

Take turns making patterns with four, five, or six shapes.

Power Up!

Learning to recognize patterns is a skill important to many content areas. This activity first emphasizes the visual recognition of patterns, then encourages students to show their understanding of the concept by creating their own patterns.

• Write the following pattern on the blackboard. Have the students help you complete it.

⬡ ○ ○ □ ○ ○ □ ___ ___ ___ ___ ___

Answers:
Power Up: ○ □ ○ ○ □ ○ ○ □ ○ ○
○ ○ □ ○ △ ○ ○ ○ □ ○ △ ○ ○
○ □ ○ ○ △ ○ ○ □ ○ △ ○ ○
□ ○ ○ △ ○ □ ○ ○ △ ○
○ □ ○ △ ○ □ ○ △ ○ △ ○

BUMPER STICKER

Power Play

1. With your partner, list five reasons why you like your school.

_____

_____

_____

_____

_____

2. Put a star next to the reason you and your partner think is the most important.
3. Rewrite that reason as a slogan for a bumper sticker.

What words do you want to write on the sticker?_____

What picture do you want to go on the sticker? _____

4. Work together to draw the bumper sticker in the space below.

Lightning Strike!

Make up different buttons that tell what you like about your school.

- -

Power Up!

Students often say what they like without thinking about why they like it. This activity is intended to encourage the students to evaluate their thoughts as they design bumper stickers for their school.

- Talk about slogans we sometimes see on bumper stickers. Tell the students they will design stickers they could use to tell others about their school.

THE BEST INVENTION

Power Play

1. With your partner, list three things that you think make a good invention.

   _____

   _____

   _____

2. List five inventions:

   _____

   _____

   _____

   _____

   _____

   Like a toaster!

3. Talk about each invention you listed. See how each one compares with what you said made a good invention.

4. Which invention do you and your partner think is the best one? _____

   Why do you think it is the best?_____

Lightning Strike!
Think of something you would like someone to invent. What would it do? Who would use it? Why would it be a good invention?

- -

Power Up!
In this activity students establish criteria for evaluation, then use this criteria in making a judgment.
- Show an invention in use in the classroom and have the children tell some things about it that make it a good invention.

WHAT COMES NEXT?

Power Play

1. When items are in **sequence** it means they are in proper order. Fill in the missing letters to complete the sequence.

A B __ D __ __ G __ __ J K __ M

__ O __ __ __ S T __ __ __ X Y Z

2. These sentences are not in sequence. Work with a partner to rearrange the sentences to form a story. Put a number from one to eleven in the blank in front of each sentence so the events occur in sequence.

Chocolate Chip Cookie Time

_____ Leon and his mother had a cold glass of milk with their cookies.

_____ Leon found a recipe in his mother's cookbook.

_____ At first the cookies were too hot to eat.

_____ They put twelve small balls of dough on each cookie sheet.

_____ Then he got out the ingredients they needed.

_____ "Can we bake cookies today?" Leon asked his mother.

_____ Leon stirred the mixture together.

_____ After ten minutes, the cookies were ready to take out of the oven.

_____ Leon's mother helped him put the cookies in the oven.

_____ "Yes," she said, "if you will help."

_____ After they ate their cookies, they cleaned up the kitchen together.

Lightning Strike!

How does putting things in order help them make more sense? What other things could you put in order?

- -

Power Up!

Students learn that numbers and letters follow a specific sequence. To make sense, the events in a story need to follow a sequence also.

- Make a copy of a short poem or story. Cut the page so each sentence is on a separate strip of paper. Ask students to arrange the sentences in order.

Answer: 10, 3, 9, 6, 4, 1, 5, 8, 7, 2, 11

Frank Schaffer Publications

LEAFY WORDS

Power Play

Rearrange the nine letters in the leaves below to write as many words as possible. Work with a partner. Think out loud as you work. Letters may only be used once in a word. Words must be three or more letters. Continue your list on the back of this page if you need more room.

ALE _____   HALO _____   RODE _____

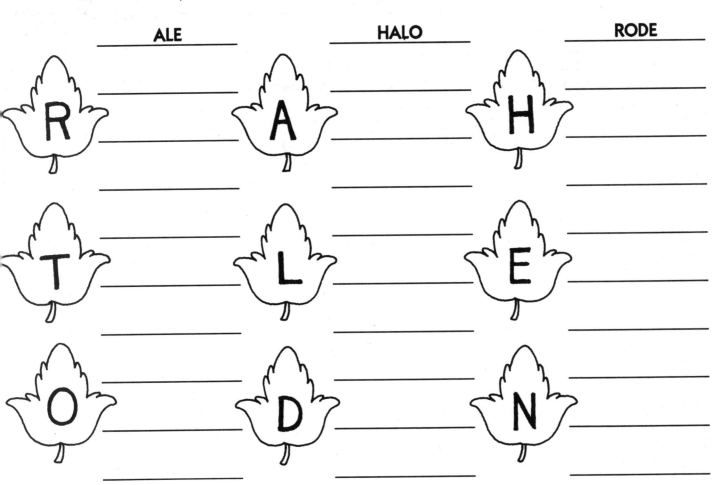

Lightning Strike!

See how many words you can make using the letters in your name.

- -

Power Up!

Students often need to mentally rearrange objects to form new combinations.

- Ask students to make a list of as many new words as they can using the letters in the name of the city or state where you live.

This is a partial list of words that can be formed: alone, ant, ante, are, art, ate, dare, dart, date, dead, deal, dean, dear, den, dole, done, dot, dote, ear, earl, eat, end, era, hale, haled, halt, hard, hare, hat, hate, hated, head, heal, hear, heard, heart, held, hen, herd, hold, hole, hone, honed, hot, hen, land, lane, lard, late, lead, lean, led, let, load, loan, lode, lone, lord, lot, Nat, Nate, near, neat, Ned, net, node, not, noted, oar, oath, ode, old, one, ran, rant, ranted, rat, rate, rated, read, real, red, road, roan, rode, role, rot, rote, tan, tea, tear, Ted, ten, than, then, thread, toad, toe, told, ton, tone, tore, trade, tread, trod

    FS112112 POWERTHINK

CRACK THE CODE

Power Play
Kenya got four books from the library. Can you use the code to find their titles?

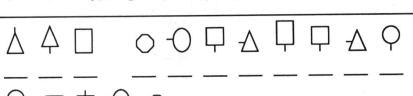

A B C D E F G H I J K L M

N O P Q R S T U V W X Y Z

1.

2.

3.

4.

Lightning Strike!
1. Take turns writing book titles in code for your partner to solve.
2. With your partner, make up your own code. Use it to write messages to each other.

Power Up!
A coded puzzle provides a fun way to apply knowledge in a new way.
- Use a book familiar to the students to demonstrate how to write a title using the code given above.

Answer Key: 1. The Drinking Gourd. 2. Time of Wonder. 3. Saint George and the Dragon. 4. Boo! Stories to Make You Jump.

IS THAT SO?

Power Play

1. A **fact** is something you can prove to be true. You can look it up in a dictionary, encyclopedia, or other book of facts. An **opinion** is something you cannot prove to be true. You cannot look it up in a book. It only tells what someone else thinks or feels about something else. Talk with your partner about the difference between facts and opinions.

2. Look at an advertisement. See if you can tell if part of it is fact and part is opinion.

What is being advertised? _____

Facts: _____

_____

_____

Opinions: _____

_____

_____

Lightning Strike!

1. Look for facts and opinions in a TV advertisement.
2. Write two advertisements. Use facts in one and opinions in the other.

- -

Power Up!

Distinguishing fact from opinion is an important thinking skill that students need both now and later in life.

- Write the words "fact" and "opinion" on the board and have children name a topic and suggest examples for both.
- Provide newspaper or magazine advertisements for each group.
- Have students bring in copies of ads. Hold a group discussion about which parts are facts and which are opinions.

WHERE TO LOOK

Power Play

1. Libraries have different places for different kinds of books.
   Fiction books are stories that are made up by authors.
   Nonfiction books contain facts. They tell about real people, places, or things.
   Reference books contain information.
2. In what part of the library would you look to find a book with the kind of information listed below? Write the correct letter in the space in front of each book.

F for Fiction   **N** for Nonfiction   **R** for Reference

____ A fairy tale

____ What a word means

____ A story with a horse in it

____ Science experiments

____ All about airplanes

____ Lots of pictures of different kinds of sharks

____ A page or two about horses

____ How to say a word

____ A map of your state

____ The birthdate of Abraham Lincoln

Lightning Strike!

1. Write down the titles of different kinds of books. Have your partner tell you what kind of books they are.
2. Find out if your library has other ways to divide books and other materials. Write down what they are. Give examples of what kind of library materials you find in each area.

Power Up!

As students learn what resources are available in a library and how to use them, they will be more aware of sources for problem solving and other types of material.

- Take the class to the library. Ask the librarian to show students where to find different types of books.

WHAT A CHARACTER!

Power Play

1. Think of a book or story that both you and your partner have read.

_____

2. Write the names of three main characters in the book.
3. Write words that describe the main characters.

Names of Main Characters	What the Main Characters Are Like

I'm loaded with all kinds of characters!

Lightning Strike!

How does each character change in the story? Does the character affect the story by the way he or she acts? Draw a picture of how you think one of these characters looks.

- -

Power Up!

Students can better comprehend a story if they are able to understand its individual parts. This activity encourages students to describe a story's main characters in order to see how such characters contribute to the story as a whole.

- Review the meaning of the word "character."
- Write down the main characters from a story recently read by the students. Have the students suggest words that tell what these main characters are like.

JUMP INTO A PICTURE

Power Play

1. Look at the picture. Talk about what it would be like to walk into it. What would you look like? What would you do? What would happen to you there?
2. Write a story about your adventure inside the picture on the back of this page.

Welcome to Planet Zorbit

Lightning Strike!

Combine the activity with an art project. Draw yourself in the picture.

Power Up!

Children learn to take a creative jump by putting together different components to make a new whole. The activity invites the students to take a creative jump into an art picture as the basis for a writing activity.

- Show students several art pictures and invite them to comment on what it would be like to become part of the picture.
- Provide each group with an art reproduction or a book containing art reproductions. Look for subject matter of interest to students, such as families, children, boats, or animals.

DEAR DIARY

Power Play

1. Pick a book or story that you and your partner have read.
2. Select one of the main characters in the book. Talk about what might have happened to the character five years after the end of the book.
3. Write down what the character might have said about one day five years later.

Day:_____

_____

_____

_____

_____

_____

_____

_____

_____

_____

Lightning Strike!

Write about other events that might have happened to this character or another character after the story ended. Keep your own diary. Write in it every day. Go back and read what you wrote a month from now or a year from now.

- -

Power Up!

Using the diary as a format, this activity encourages students to predict what might happen to a character after a story ends.

- Explain that a diary is a daily written record of what happens to a person. If possible, show them an example of a diary or a journal.
- Review the meaning of the word "character."

Name(s)_____

AS LARGE AS A WHALE

Power Play

1. Authors often use the words "like" and "as" to give readers a clear picture. Read these two examples:

> The sun was like a golden ball.
> Jessie ran as fast as a race car.

2. When the words "like" or "as" are used in a phrase, it is called a **simile**. Work with your partner to write ten similes.

1. The fish was as big as _____.

2. The wind blew as hard as _____.

3. Sandy hopped up and down like _____.

4. The stormy sea was as black as _____.

5. The white fluffy clouds were like _____.

6. The mountain was as high as _____.

7. Jeremy ran as fast as _____.

8. Sara jumped as high as _____.

9. The shadow looked like _____.

10. The circus clowns were as funny as _____.

Lightning Strike!

How do similes paint pictures with words? Read your two best similes to the class. Listen to other similes your classmates have written. Watch for similes as you read.

Power Up!

Students often find that similes give a clearer picture of a word than other types of definitions because of the word pictures they present.

- Explain the word "simile" and give students several examples.
- Explain the difference between a dictionary definition and a simile. Talk about how similes make a story more interesting.

TIME OF WONDER

Power Play

1. Why do you think Robert McClosky called his book *Time of Wonder*?

_____

_____

_____

2. Do you think it was a "time of wonder"? _____

   Why or why not? _____

_____

_____

3. Write about a place you went to that was a "time of wonder" for you.

_____

_____

_____

_____

_____

_____

Lightning Strike!

Cut a piece of paper in half. Fold and staple the two halves together to make a book. Write the story of your own "time of wonder" on the pages. Draw pictures to go with the story.

Power Up!

Students need to be able to relate what they read to their own lives. After evaluating what made the time so special in the book, they can think of a time in their own lives that was a "time of wonder."

- Read the book <u>Time of Wonder</u> by Robert McClosky (Puffin, 1989), which tells about the summer spent by two girls on an island in Maine.

SCHOOL FLAG

Power Play

1. Talk about the kind of pictures and words found on flags that you have seen.
2. What would you like your flag to tell about your school?

_____

3. What pictures and words could you use to show what you want to tell about your school?

_____   _____

_____   _____

4. Put a star by the pictures and words that you decide to use on your school flag.
5. Use the space below to draw the outline of your flag.
6. Draw and color your flag on a large piece of paper.
7. Tell the rest of the class about your flag.

Lightning Strike!

1. Make a flag for your class or group.
2. Make a flag out of fabric or paper scraps.
3. Besides countries and states, what other places or groups might have their own flags?

Power Up!

This activity encourages the students to take information they have learned about flags and create a new one for their school.

- Show pictures of flags used by the United States and other countries. Talk about state flags and explain the meaning of your own state flag.
- Provide each group with a large piece of paper and crayons.
- Put the school flags made by your class along the hallway outside your room.

WHAT'S YOUR ENVIRONMENT?

Power Play

1. The word **environment** means the land, water, and weather in an area.
2. What is the environment where you live?

Land_____

_____

Water_____

_____

Weather_____

_____

3. How does the environment where you live affect you? Think about things you do, games you play, what you wear, and what plants and animals share your environment.

_____

_____

_____

_____

_____

Lightning Strike!

What are some ways people change the environment? How have people changed the environment in the area where you live?

Power Up!

Students examine ways the environment of the area where they live affects them. They look beyond themselves at the larger picture.

* Discuss how different environments might affect what people wear, what types of recreation they enjoy, what types of pets they keep, and even what foods they eat most.

BOTH SIDES

Power Play

1. An **opinion** is what someone thinks about a subject. You have opinions on many things, like your favorite food, what colors you like, and what games you like to play.
2. List two other things you could have an opinion about.

_____

_____

3. Not everyone agrees with one another. We all have different opinions. That's okay. When you listen to other opinions, you can learn more about other people. Sometimes, listening to another opinion may lead you to change your mind.
4. Do you think a class should have one teacher for all subjects? Would it be better if a class had a different teacher for each subject? Work with a partner to think of reasons for both questions.

Reasons why a class should have one teacher for all subjects	Reasons why a class should have a different teacher for each subject

_____   _____

_____   _____

_____   _____

_____   _____

_____   _____

Lightning Strike!

Think of another topic that people could have different opinions about. Work with a partner to think of reasons for both sides.

- -

Power Up!

Students need to learn that most issues have more than one side and to be able to see things from another's viewpoint.

- Hold a class discussion on this statement: To really know a person, you need to walk a mile in his shoes.

Name(s)_____

A NEW ENVIRONMENT

Power Play

1. Many different environments are found in our country. Think of reasons why you would like to live in each environment listed. Give reasons why you might not like to live there. If needed, look in a book for information about the environment.

Environment	Why I Would Like to Live There	Why I Would Not Like to Live There
Desert		
Mountain		
Plain		
Wetland		
Grassland		
Forest		

2. Look at your list. If you lived in an environment different from your own, which one would you choose? Why?

_____

_____

Lightning Strike!

Draw your partner and yourself in your new environment.

- -

Power Up!

Students need an opportunity to make personal judgments about the materials they have studied.

- Talk about some of the different environments you have learned about in your class this year.
- Provide books telling about different environments found in our country.
- Provide each group with crayons.
- Provide books on different areas of the country.

GROUP THINK

Power Play

To **brainstorm** means to work together to think of as many ideas about a subject as you can. By combining your brainpower, you can come up with many new ideas.

1. Work in small groups. Select one of the topics listed. Take turns talking about the topic.
2. Have one member of the group write down all the ideas. Use the back of this page or another sheet of paper.

    A. How can people of different backgrounds learn to get along together better?

    B. What does it mean to be a responsible person?

    C. Sometimes we get angry at people or situations. What are some ways to deal with anger?

Lightning Strike!

What was your group's best idea? Why did you like that idea best?

Power Up!

Brainstorming in groups helps students combine their thinking skills. An idea by one member of the group often sparks new ideas by other members. This technique is useful in many areas.

- Divide the students into groups of three or four. Walk around the class as students work and encourage them if they seem to get stumped.

OUR RESOURCES

Power Play
1. Resources are things found in the environment that people use, like water, plants, and animals.
2. What resources can be found in the area where you live? List them and tell how they are used.

Resources	How They Are Used
_____	_____
_____	_____
_____	_____
_____	_____
_____	_____
_____	_____
_____	_____
_____	_____
_____	_____

Lightning Strike!
1. Make a poster showing the resources of your community.
2. Think of some ways you use these resources.

Power Up!
An important thinking skill for students to develop is the ability to look at and categorize what they see around them.
- Review the meaning of the word *resource*. Have the students give examples of resources and the parts of the country in which they are found.
- Put a map of your area on the bulletin board. Attach pictures of different resources to where they are found on the map.

MAP IT OUT

Power Play

1. Lines, dots, and pictures are used as symbols to show information on a map. The legend tells what these symbols mean.
2. Decide on a place in your community to show on a map. You could show your schoolyard, a park, a playground, or your neighborhood.
3. What place will you show on your map?

_____

What symbols will you use on your map?

_____

4. Draw the map. Draw the symbols used on the map in the legend.

Legend

Lightning Strike!

1. Draw a map that shows how to get to a place you would like to go.
2. Draw a map that will lead to a make-believe treasure!
3. Draw a map of a building.

 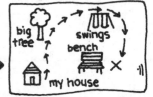

Power Up!

After learning information, students need to know how to use it in new ways.

* Show students a state map. Point out the legend and explain what the symbols mean.

SHAPE PUZZLE

Power Play
Work together to find the answers. (Hint: Count single shapes first, then count combined ones.)

1. How many boxes are in the picture below?

_____ single boxes + _____ combined boxes = _____ boxes.

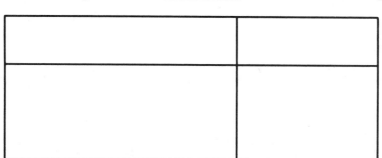

2. How many triangles are in the picture below?

_____ single triangles + _____ combined triangles = _____ triangles.

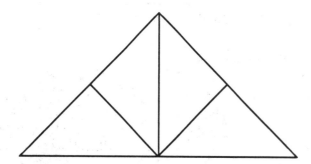

Lightning Strike!
With your partner, take turns making shape puzzles to solve.

Power Up!
This activity is designed to give students practice using a search strategy to identify the parts that make up a whole.

- Demonstrate how to count the triangles found in this diagram. Count the smaller triangles first, then the combined triangles.

Name(s)_____

TRIANGLE PUZZLE

Power Play

1. With your partner, connect the dots to see how many different triangles you can make.

.   .   .

.   .   .

.   .   .

2. Count the triangles. How many did you make? _____
    (Hint: Count single triangles first, then the combined larger ones.)

Lightning Strike!

1. How many triangles can you make from these dots?
2. Use dot paper to make shape puzzles with squares, rectangles, or other figures.

Power Up!

As students see how many different ways a triangle can be constructed from nine dots, they practice looking for different ways to use learned information.

*   Demonstrate how to make a triangle by connecting three end points with three line segments.

NUMBER PUZZLER

Power Play

Katy and Ben are throwing two balls at the bull's-eye to see who can make the most points.

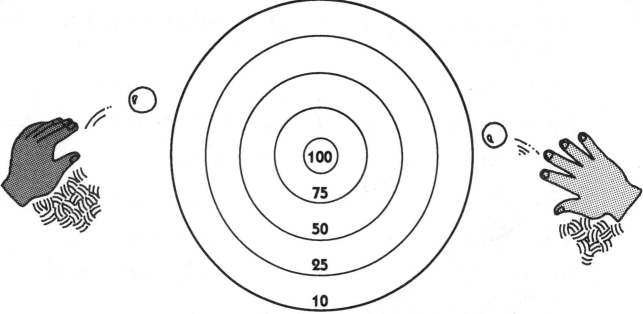

100
75
50
25
10

1. Take turns telling what two numbers Katy and Ben hit to make these points.

   175 _____ and _____   **85** _____ and _____

2. There are two ways Katy and Ben can hit 125 points using two balls. Take turns finding them.

   _____ and _____   _____ and _____

3. Can you find three different ways the children can reach 100? Think hard to find the third one!

   _____ and _____   _____ and _____   _____ and _____

Lightning Strike!

What if Katy and Ben threw three balls at the bull's-eye? Take turns writing a number made from adding three of the numbers together for your partner to solve.

Power Up!

This activity has students apply inductive reasoning as they work backwards from a final number to find the combination of numbers that add together to form it.

* Have the students find the two numbers that add together to make 150.

WHAT'S MISSING?

Power Play

What's missing in each problem? Take turns reading the problems. Tell what is missing. Write information so your partner can solve the problem.

1. Matthew wants to buy a model plane to put together. The model costs $6.98. How much more money does he need to buy the model?

   What's missing? _____

   New information:_____ Answer to problem: _____

2. The blue team made 8 goals. By how many goals did the red team win?

   What's missing? _____

   New information:_____ Answer to problem: _____

3. One class sold 156 boxes of candy. How many boxes of candy did both classes sell?

   What's missing? _____

   New information:_____ Answer to problem: _____

Lightning Strike!

Take turns writing story problems with a missing part for your partner to finish and solve.

- -

Power Up!

Students need to examine parts of a problem to see if everything they need to solve it is there. This activity asks students to identify missing information, then supply it so a mathematical procedure can be completed.

- Read the following example to the students. Ask them to identify what is missing and supply information to solve the problem.

  Jessica must sell 100 boxes of cookies to win a scout badge. How many more does she need to sell? What is missing? What information do you need to solve the problem?

SAME AND DIFFERENT

Power Play

With a partner, take turns picking two shapes from the large box.

1. Write two ways the shapes are alike.

_____
_____
_____
_____

2. Write two ways the shapes are different.

_____
_____
_____
_____

Lightning Strike!

1. Pick two shapes and find three ways they are alike or different.
2. Group shapes together that are most alike or most different.

Power Up!

Studying geometric shapes can be both an effective introduction to geometric shapes and a way to practice the thinking skill of comparing and contrasting.

- Review the geometric shapes given above. Have students name each shape and identify its unique characteristics.

HOW MANY SOLUTIONS?

Power Play

How many different addition solutions can you and your partner find for numbers from 2 to 9? See how many different ways you can add two numbers together to make the number in each box. Write your number solutions in the boxes. Have your partner check to see if you got them all. (Hint: A good way is to start with number 1 and go up until all the number combinations have been used.)

2	5	3	8
9	**4**	**6**	**7**

Lightning Strike!

1. Try this with numbers going up to 20, or higher!
2. Find solutions using three or even four numbers added together.
3. Find combinations that use subtraction to make the number you picked: Example: 5 is made from 10-5, 9-4, 8-3, 7-2, and 6-1.

Power Up!

This activity gives the students an opportunity to use inductive reasoning to look for and find different numbers that combine to make up a whole.

- Demonstrate how a combination of several different numbers will add together to make a given number. Example: 6 is formed from 1+5, 2+4, and 3+3.

GRAPH IT!

Power Play

Making a graph is a good way to show what you have counted.

Color in the grid to show how many boys and girls are in your class. Count the boys and girls in your class, then color in a rectangle for each one on the grid.

	Boys	Girls
18		
17		
16		
15		
14		
13		
12		
11		
10		
9		
8		
7		
6		
5		
4		
3		
2		
1		

Lightning Strike!

Find something else in your classroom to count and record on a grid. Count the objects. Draw a grid and color in the numbers you counted.

- -

Power Up!

Graphing is a simple way for students to transpose information into a form that is easily understood.
- Draw a one-column grid on the board. Demonstrate how to color in each section of the grid as you count several similar things in the room.
- Provide crayons or colored pencils for each group.

SOCK DETECTIVE

41

Power Play
What color socks are your classmates wearing today? Is there a difference between the color of socks boys and girls wear? Use a table to find out this information.

1. Complete this table to show what kind of socks your classmates are wearing. Assign one partner to count the colors of socks the boys are wearing and the other to count the colors of socks the girls are wearing. Fill in the table. Don't forget to count yourself and your partner.

Children	Color of Socks				
Boys					
Girls					

2. What did you learn?
    What color of socks did most of your classmates have on today? _____

    What color of socks did most girls wear today? _____

    What color of socks did most boys wear today? _____

Lightning Strike!
Find something else in your classroom to count. Make a table to show the numbers you counted.

Power Up!
Once students gather information, they need to know how to use it. Organizing and evaluating information is the goal of this activity.

*   Review the construction of a table to use in gathering information. An example to work with might be the color of the students' hair or eyes.

LIMA BEAN SURPRISE

Power Play

Graphs give people a clear picture of numbers. One type is called a **pie chart** because it is round and divided into pieces. A pie chart shows how a large number can be broken down into smaller groups.

1. Study this example: In the school election,
   50 students voted for Troy.
   100 students voted for Marge.
   150 students voted for Terry.

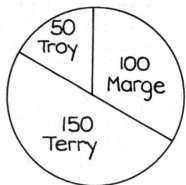

2. Study the pie chart. The whole pie equals all the students who voted. The pieces of the pie equal the number who voted for Troy, Marge, and Terry.

3. Read the information below. Work with a partner to complete the pie chart.

   On Monday
   25 students had cookies for dessert.
   50 had Jello.
   75 had ice cream.
   150 had pie.
   200 had Lima Bean Surprise.

Dessert Choices

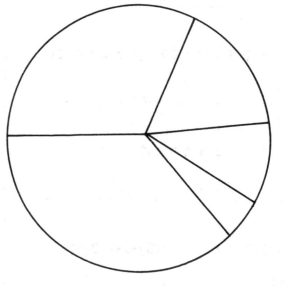

Lightning Strike!

What other types of information could you show with a pie chart? How does a pie chart help you see who got the most votes or which dessert most students chose?

Power Up!

Graphs provide a visual representation of numbers, allowing students to see a relationship among numbers and a breakdown of a large quantity almost instantly.

* Show students different examples of pie charts and explain how the sizes of the pieces are determined.

Name(s)_____

WHAT A BEAUTIFUL BABY!

Power Play
What do you know about baby animals?
1. Cut out the cards on the bottom of the page. Put the cards in a pile.
2. Take turns turning the cards over. Read what the card says about a baby animal. Give an example of a baby animal that matches.
3. After you have gone through the cards once, mix them up and go through them a second time naming different animals.

Lightning Strike!
1. Give yourself a point each time you name an animal. See who can reach 21 points first.
2. Pick a card and see who can list the most animals to go with the statement.
3. Find out more about baby animals. Make cards to tell about them.

Lives in a pouch	Hatches from a hard-shelled egg
Eats worms brought by its parents	Eats the leaf it hatches on
Born blind	Drinks milk from its mother
Hatches from a jelly-like egg	Born with eyes open
Never knows its mother	Stays with its mother

Power Up!
One way to go beyond basic facts is to think of examples to go with a description.
• Compare the ways animal parents care for their babies.

FS112112 POWERTHINK

Frank Schaffer Publications

A WHOZIWHAT

Power Play

Your great-great-grandfather, the inventor, sent you a large package for your birthday. You open it and find a strange machine. He didn't send any instructions. You hope this is something better than the automatic shoe shiner that shined shoes, but ate shoe laces.

Study the picture of great-great-grandpa's invention. Work in a small group to see if you can figure out what it does. Talk about your ideas. Ask one member of the group to write the ideas on another sheet of paper.

Lightning Strike!

1. Which idea did you like the best? Write reasons why you liked that idea.
2. What is the first thing you would do if you received something like this in the mail?
3. Design a Whoziwhat of your own and explain what it does.

- -

Power Up!

In this activity students brainstorm to think of possible uses for an unknown machine. They apply what they know about machines they have used previously.

- Talk about how ideas from one member of a group can lead to new ideas for other members.
- Divide the students into groups of three or four for this activity.

PLANTS AND ANIMALS

Power Play

1. Take turns flipping a coin. If you flip heads, describe one way plants and animals are alike. If you flip tails, describe one way plants and animals are different.
2. With a partner, fill in the chart below.

Plants and Animals	
Ways They Are Alike	**Ways They Are Different**

Lightning Strike!

1. Make a poster showing how plants and animals are alike or different.
2. Pick two different animals or plants. Make a chart showing how they are the same or different.

- -

Power Up!

"How are they alike? How are they different?" Learning to compare and contrast items are important critical thinking skills for students to develop.

- Provide each group with a coin.

WHAT'S THAT DOING HERE?

Power Play
One animal is out of place in each picture. Work with your partner to find it and finish the sentences.

A. The _____ is not born alive.

B. The _____ is not hatched from an egg.

A.

B.

Lightning Strike!
Cut the pictures apart. Take turns putting two animals that are alike in some way in a row with a third picture that does not belong. Have your partner find the picture that does not belong and tell why it doesn't belong.

Power Up!
Learning to tell what is out of place is an important thinking skill for students to develop. This activity has students analyze groups of animals to see what makes them alike and what makes them different.

ENDANGERED ANIMALS

Power Play

1. Some animals are in danger of becoming extinct. Take turns explaining why the animal is endangered.

leopard   elephant   American crocodile
rhinoceros   panda   tiger
orangutan

2. Pick an animal that is endangered. (It does not have to be on this list.)
One of you draws a picture of the animal while the other writes a speech bubble telling what the animal might say if it could talk.

Lightning Strike!

1. Design a wanted poster the animal might make for the kind of person causing it to become extinct.
2. Make a book about endangered animals. Tell why the animals are endangered and what might be done to save them.
3. List reasons why it is important to save animals from extinction.

Power Up!

This activity provides a format for students to practice synthesis, the transformation of information they have learned into a new form.

- Discuss some reasons animals are becoming extinct.
- Discuss efforts being made to save animals from extinction.

Name(s)_____

SEARCHING FOR NUMBER 1

Power Play

1. With your partner, list five important plants. Think of ways they are used and write them below.

Plants	Use
_____	_____
_____	_____
_____	_____
_____	_____
_____	_____

2. To **rank** means to place things in order by what is most important. Look over your list with your partner. Decide which plant is the most important. Put a number 1 by it. Number the other plants 2 through 5 in the order of their importance.

3. Tell why your number-one plant is most important. _____

_____

I'm so honored!

Most Useful Plant Award

Jeremy Olsen

Lightning Strike!

1. Write the award to be given to the most useful plant.
2. What other plants help us?
3. List other kinds of helpers. With your partner, decide on the most important ones.

- -

Power Up!

Students need to learn to prioritize items in order of importance. This activity encourages students to evaluate different plants by using them as a basis for ranking by importance.

- Discuss different types of plants and their uses. Include plants used for food, clothing, medicine, and habitats.
- Explain the meaning of the word rank and demonstrate its use.

WEATHER WATCH

Power Play

1. Be a junior weather person! Use the chart below to record the weather for a week.

Day	Weather			
	Sun	Clouds	Amount of Rain or Snow	Temperature
Monday				
Tuesday				
Wednesday				
Thursday				
Friday				

2. At the end of the week, look at the weather chart. What kind of day was most common?

_____

Based on this week, what do you think next week will be like? Pretend you and your partner are weather forecasters. Write your forecast. Share it with the class.

_____

Lightning Strike!

1. Keep a record for the weather for two weeks, a month, or longer.
2. Draw your own chart and use your own symbols to show what the weather was like each day.
3. Check the newspaper or TV for the daily weather. Write a daily weather forecast to put up in your classroom. Was the forecast correct?
4. Write a forecast for the kind of weather you like best.

Power Up!

Learning to record information in a meaningful fashion is an important skill used in many different subject areas.

- Review how to read and record information on a chart.
- Provide a thermometer for checking the temperature.

TROUBLE WITH CAPITAL T

Power Play

1. Cut out the pieces of the puzzle below.
2. Arrange the four puzzle pieces to form a capital T. Be patient and keep trying. It can be done.

This could be tricky...

Lightning Strike!

When you have found the solution, don't show it to others. Let them try to figure it out for themselves. Share this puzzle with family members and friends.

- -

Power Up!

This puzzle can be difficult for both children and adults. There is only one right answer, but completing it may require trying many combinations. Watching how students tackle this puzzle tells you much about the steps they use to solve problems. If some students become frustrated, suggest they try turning some of the pieces over.

LIGHT TO DARK

51

Power Play

1. Fold over the black piece of paper. Make marks 1 inch (2.5 cm) apart along all but the folded side.
2. Cut lines from the fold to 1 inch (2.5 cm) from the opposite end.
3. Cut several strips from each different shade of color.
4. Arrange the colors from light to dark.
5. Starting at the left, weave your first strip under, then over, then under, then over. Continue this pattern until you reach the other side. Weave the next strip just the opposite. Weave over, under, over, under, etc. Continue alternating these two patterns until your mat is finished.
6. Glue the ends of the strips down when you are done.

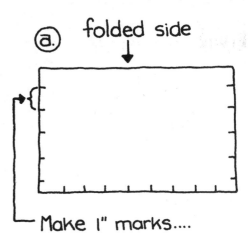

ⓐ **folded side**

Make 1" marks....

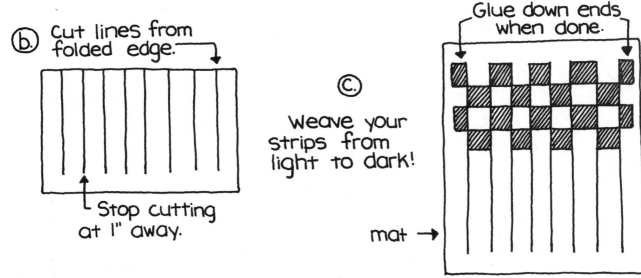

ⓑ **Cut lines from folded edge.**

Stop cutting at 1" away.

ⓒ Weave your strips from light to dark!

Glue down ends when done.

mat →

Lightning Strike!

Use paint to show light and shade. Put the same color in a row of egg carton cups. Add a few drops of white to one egg cup. Add more white to the next cup. Add a few drops of black to one paint cup. Add more black to the next cup. Paint strips of different shades of color onto a piece of paper to show how the color changes from light to dark. Or paint a sunset picture with your shaded colors.

Power Up!

Organizing shades of color provides practice in the skill of categorizing.

- Demonstrate how to weave a strip of paper in and out of slits cut into another sheet. Repeat with a second strip to show how to alternate the weaving pattern.
- Use objects in the room to demonstrate the gradations of color from light to dark.
- Provide each group with one black piece of paper, three pieces of paper in different shades of one color (example: pink, bright red, dark red), a ruler, scissors, pencil, and glue.

FS112112 POWERTHINK   Frank Schaffer Publications

COLOR WORDS

Power Play

1. What words can you think of to describe a color? Take turns naming a color and thinking of words to describe it.
2. Write words to describe each color listed below. Use words from the Word Box or words of your own. Think about how the colors make you feel.

Word Box
loud   wild   quiet   calm   noisy   happy   sad   peaceful   cool   warm   hot   icy

Red _____

Orange _____

Yellow _____

Green _____

Blue _____

Purple _____

3. With your partner, pick a word from the Word Box. Write the word on another sheet of paper. Choose colors that fit your word. Make the word into a picture.

Lightning Strike!

Think of three colors that seem warm. List some objects that are warm colors. Think of three colors that seem cool. What objects are usually found in cool colors?

- -

Power Up!

Students analyze and compare the effects of different colors in this activity.
- Demonstrate the effect of color by showing them two objects in different colors.
  Examples: A red shirt and a blue shirt or bright, bold and soft, warm colored wallpaper samples.
- Ask them to describe how the same object in different colors changes the way they feel about it.
- Provide paper and crayons for each group.

CHOOSING A LINE

Power Play

1. With a partner, take turns drawing a line above each word.

Zig-zag	**Curved**	**Straight**	**Wavy**

2. Some lines seem quiet, some seem wild, and some are in between. With your partner, fill in the names of the lines, from quiet to wild, in the blanks below.

_____ _____ _____ _____

Quiet ➤━━━━━━━━━━━━━━━━━━━━━━━━━━━━━━━━━━━➤ **Wild**

3. Take turns drawing a line and having your partner make a picture from the line.

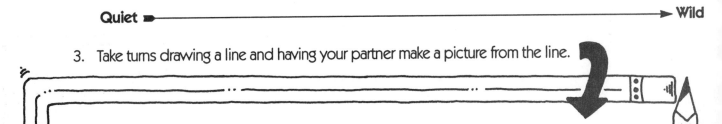

Lightning Strike!

Why are lines drawn down the middle of a road? What kind of lines are used on different types of road signs? Are you more likely to read words in a box drawn with heavy bold lines than with thin lines? List some other ways lines are used to get your attention. How does the shape of a line affect how much attention you pay to it?

Power Up!

Students need to distinguish between the different effects that lines can produce in order to better choose how to use these lines in the pictures they make. This activity provides practice in using evaluation as the basis for decision-making.

• Provide children with crayons and paper.

LINES AND COLORS

Power Play

Draw a picture in the box that uses lines and colors to show a word.

1. With your partner, pick the word your picture will be about. Write your word on the title line.
2. Decide what kind of lines and colors you will use to show the word.

Kinds of lines: _____

Colors: _____

3. Decide who will draw the lines and who will color the spaces.
4. Draw the lines and color the spaces.

Title _____

Lightning Strike!

Study the lines and colors used on packages and labels at a grocery store. How do people who design packages and labels use lines and colors to get your attention?

- -

Power Up!

Putting knowledge together in a new way allows students to combine their knowledge of line and color to make a specific kind of picture.

- Review the way color and line can express feelings.
- Provide crayons for each group.

THE UNKNOWN TREASURE

Power Play

Kim and Kelly followed a map and found this treasure chest at the spot marked with an **X**. When they opened it, they were surprised to not find gold, silver, or jewels. They were very happy about what they did find.

What did Kim and Kelly find in the treasure chest? Talk with your partner about what they might have found. Work together to draw the objects in the chest.

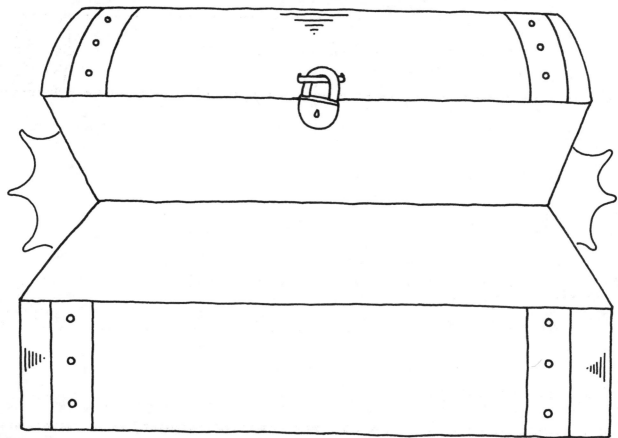

Lightning Strike!

What else could Kim and Kelly have found in the treasure chest? If you could have anything in the world, what would it be? Describe the one thing you would want most and tell why it is important to you.

- -

Power Up!

In this activity students use their imaginations to speculate about a buried treasure. They use thinking skills to evaluate and prioritize when making a decision on what they would like most.

- Ask students to share their choices about what would be most important to them and explain why these things are important.
- Post drawings for others to enjoy.

WHAT'S THE PROBLEM?

Power Play
To solve a problem, you need to be able to tell what the problem is. Be problem detectives. Cut the cards apart and put them in a pile. Take turns with your partner turning the cards over and reading them. Have your partner tell you what the problem is.

Lightning Strike!
Take turns going through the cards again. Think of solutions to each problem. Choose the best one and write it on the other side of the card.

You look in your desk for your math paper. You don't know where it could be.

What is your problem?

You have $2.00. The new movie costs $3.25.

What is your problem?

You have $.50 to spend at the garage sale. A poster costs $.30. A joke book costs $.40.

What is your problem?

Your mother wants you to clean your room on Saturday morning. Your friends are going skating on Saturday morning.

What is your problem?

Amy wants you to play with her. Jeffrey wants you to play with him.

What is your problem?

You have to sell ten boxes of candy for Scouts. You have sold five.

What is your problem?

Power Up!
The first step to problem solving is identifying the problem. The following game provides students with practice in explaining what the problem is in their own words.

- Explain that, in order to solve a problem, we have to know what the problem is. Read the following situation and have the students tell you what the problem is. "You are looking through the glass at different kinds of ice cream. You think the strawberry and the chocolate ice cream look best of all. What is your problem?"
- Provide each group with a pair of scissors.

HOW TO SOLVE A PROBLEM

Power Play

1. Take turns reading these four steps for problem solving.
   a. Identify the problem.
   b. List solutions to the problem.
   c. Look at each solution to see if it will work.
   d. Pick the best solution to try. If it doesn't work, pick another.
2. Read what happened to Mimi. Work together to follow the first three steps.

Mimi's bus came to pick her up but Mimi was not there to meet it.

1. What's the problem? _____

2. List the things that Mimi could do to solve her problem.

_____

_____

_____

_____

_____

3. Put a star by what you think is the best solution to the problem.
4. What if this solution doesn't work? Put an **X** by the solution you and your partner think Mimi should try next.

Lightning Strike!

Think of a problem you need to solve. Follow the four steps as you write down how you might solve it. Try the solution you pick as the best one. Share how it worked with your partner.

Power Up!

Following a sequence of steps can lead students to an appropriate solution.
- Review the four steps to problem solving given on this page.

AT THE MEET

Power Play

1. Joe, David, and Matthew are swimming in a meet. Each of them can be in only two races. You are helping the coach work out what races each boy can swim in. Put a check in the table to help you solve the problem. Take turns checking one sentence at a time on the table until you find the answer to the problem.

    The coach had time trials to see which race the boys should be in. Joe was best in the butterfly stroke. David was best in the backstroke. Matthew was best in freestyle. Matthew was slowest in the butterfly stroke. Joe was slowest at the backstroke.

    What will David's second race be? _____

	Freestyle	Backstroke	Butterfly
Joe			
David			
Matthew			

2. Work together to make your own table to solve this problem:
    You need to give a ribbon to the winner of one of the swimming races. Latasha, Amy, and Mary swam in the freestyle race. Latasha was not third. Amy was second. Mary was not first.

    Who won the race? _____

Lightning Strike!

With a partner, make up your own word problems for each other to solve.

- -

Power Up!

Students need to learn different strategies to solve problems. One solution is to make a table to illustrate the problem. This exercise demonstrates how a table can help solve the problem of who swims in which races.

Name(s)_____

FLOWER GARDEN

Power Play

1. Plan a flower garden. First look at different colored flowers you could plant. Take turns reading about the plants. Have one partner highlight the color and the other partner highlight the height of each plant.

Plants:
Painted Daisy: Red or pink petals. Grows 2-3 feet (61-91 cm) tall.
Black-eyed Susan: Yellow petals. Grows 2 feet (61 cm) tall.
Blue flax: Sky-blue flowers. Grows 18-24 inches (46-61 cm) tall.
Hollyhock: Comes in yellow, pink, lilac, and white. Grows 5-8 feet (152-245 cm) tall.
Lily: Comes in orange, red, pink, yellow, and purple. Grows 4 feet (122 cm) tall.
Mum: Comes in yellow, red, white, purple, and orange. Grows 24-30 inches (61-76 cm) tall.

2. With your partner, fill out this table to help you choose three flowers to use in the garden.

Color	Flower	Height
_____	_____	_____
_____	_____	_____
_____	_____	_____

3. Turn the paper over. Work together to outline the garden and the spot where the three kinds of flowers will go. Color in the color of the flowers you will plant.

Lightning Strike!

1. Look in seed catalogs or flower books for other kinds of flowers you could plant in a garden. Design a garden with more colors and kinds of flowers.
2. Design a garden with plants that grow in shade.

Power Up!

Highlighting special information can help students evaluate data. Making a table and picture are other useful solution strategies for problem solving.

• Provide each group with crayons and a highlighter marker.

CHOOSING A MEAL

Power Play

You are trying to decide what combination to get for your meal at a restaurant. The meal comes with three items: French fries; a hamburger or cheeseburger; and lemonade, shake, or milk.

With your partner, construct an organized list to help you see what different meals you could get.

French fries   +   _____   +   _____

French fries   +   _____   +   _____

French fries   +   _____   +   _____

French fries   +   _____   +   _____

French fries   +   _____   +   _____

French fries   +   _____   +   _____

Lightning Strike!

What choices do you have in your school lunchroom? With your partner, write the choices for one lunch. Write an organized list to show the combinations you could buy for lunch.

Power Up!

An organized list is an easy way for students to work out problems involving a variety of choices.

• Demonstrate how to make an organized list, using the following example:
Sandy is undecided about what to wear today. She could wear her pink T-shirt or her yellow T-shirt with her green shorts or her blue shorts. What combinations of shorts and shirt can she make?

pink T-shirt + green shorts   yellow T-shirt + green shorts

pink T-shirt + blue shorts   yellow T-shirt + blue shorts

WHERE DOES THE TIME GO?

Power Play

You want to use your time better at school to do homework. Make a circle graph to help you find times when you can work on homework during school time.

1. With your partner, divide the circle graph to show what you do during your day at school.

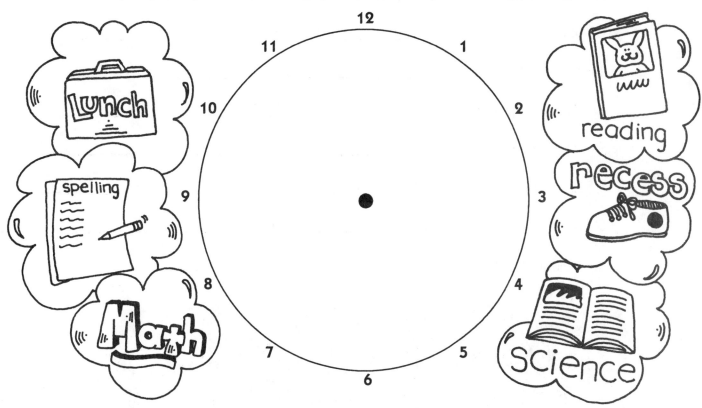

2. Look at the circle graph. What are the times you can work on homework during school time? Mark them with the highlighter.

Lightning Strike!

Make a circle graph to help you plan what to do after school. Make a list of things you want or have to do. Don't forget time for homework! Write down the time it takes to do each one. Show your list to your partner. Mark when you will do each one on a circle graph.

Power Up!

A circle graph, another problem-solving strategy, is an effective way for students to record time blocks in a format that is meaningful for them to comprehend.

- Demonstrate how to draw a circle, number the hours around it, then draw in lines that divide the circle into different time periods.
- Provide each group with a highlighter and a ruler.

Frank Schaffer Publicat'

DETECTIVE AT WORK

Power Play

Be a detective. Here are ways to solve problems. Tell the kinds of problems they can solve.

Take turns picking one of the problem solvers. Read it to your partner. Have your partner write down an example of a problem that could be solved with that problem solver.

Problem Solvers	Problem to Be Solved
1. Make a list.	_____
2. Make an organized list.	_____
3. Draw a picture.	_____
4. Draw a circle graph.	_____
5. Make a table.	_____
6. Brainstorm solutions.	_____

Lightning Strike!

Do you know other ways to solve problems? List them. Take turns with your partner, thinking of a problem each of them can solve.

- -

Power Up!

Students need to know not only different problem-solving strategies, but how and when to use them. This exercise encourages students to find different ways in which some of these strategies can be used.

- Review the problem-solving strategies found on this page.

ENCOURAGING POWERTHINKING

One of the additional benefits of teaching critical thinking and problem solving in your classroom is that it is an excellent forum for positive reinforcement. Try some of these on for size!

That's an excellent question.

Perhaps that idea would work. Let's try it.

That's a creative way of looking at it.

Not many people would have come up with such an unusual idea.

Terrific idea!

Very interesting thought! Maybe it would work.

I never thought of it that way. Good idea!

That could be just the ticket!

That suggestion makes a lot of sense.

That idea is pretty fantastic.

What a wonderful thought!

That suggestion is quite unique.

That shows you're really thinking.

Let's consider Joe's idea.

Very imaginative!

Splendid!

What a marvelous plan!

Let's consider Sue's recommendation.

Very creative!

Let's give Kim a round of applause for that suggestion.

Very inventive!

Let's follow Tim's line of thinking and see where it goes.

Now why didn't I think of that? Good job.

How did you ever think of such a good idea?

Congratulations on coming up with that solution.

You're very observant!

Your good ideas are popping like popcorn.

That could be just the answer we need.

All right!

That idea shows you're really thinking.

You're quite a **POWERTHINKER.**

Your question shows you put a lot of thought into the problem.

You're really thinking today!

Good going!

That's a pretty awesome idea!

Brilliant idea!

You're very creative.

Great plan!

I knew you could figure out an answer for yourself.

You handled that tough problem very well.

Wow! I'm impressed.

You made a wise decision.

You handled that problem well.

Brilliant!

Jill has the hang of it now.

What an interesting proposal!

This class is full of good ideas today.

See what you can accomplish!

Working together really works.

Well done!

I can't believe all the great ideas you've had today.

Nice job!

Keep up the good work.

That is so outrageous it's contagious!

BIBLIOGRAPHY

Teacher Books

Beyer, Barry K. Practical Strategies for the Teaching of Thinking.
    Boston: Allyn and Bacon, 1987.
Bloom, Benjamin, et al. Taxonomy of Educational Objectives: Handbook 1: Cognitive Domain.
    New York: David McKay, 1956.
Costa, Arthur L. Developing Minds: A Resource Book for Teaching Thinking, Volumes 1& 2.
    Washington, DC: Association for Supervision and Curriculum Development, 1991.
Heiman, Marcia and Joshua Slomianko, eds. Thinking Skills Instruction: Concepts and Techniques.
    Washington, DC: National Education Association, 1987.
Heiman, Marcia and Joshua Slomianko. Critical Thinking Skills.
    Washington, DC: National Education Association, 1986.
Moore, Brooke Noel and Richard Parker. Critical Thinking.
    Mountain View, CA: Mayfield Publishing Company, 1986.
Raths, Louis E., et al. Teaching for Thinking: Theory, Strategies & Activities for the Classroom.
    New York: Columbia University, 1986.
Stiggins, Richard J.; Rubel, Evelyn; and Quellmalz, Edys. Measuring Thinking Skills in the Classroom.
    Washington, DC: National Education Association, 1986.
Van Oech, Roger. A Kick in the Seat of the Pants.
    New York: Harper & Row, 1986.
Van Oech, Roger. A Whack on the Side of the Head.
    New York: Harper & Row, 1985.
Curriculum Update
    Washington, DC: Association for Supervision and Curriculum Developement, June, 1993.

Student Books

Berry, Joy. Every Kid's Guide to Thinking and Learning.
    Chicago: Childrens Press, 1987.
Berry, Joy. Every Kid's Guide to Decision Making and Problem Solving.
    Chicago: Childrens Press, 1987.
Berry, Joy. Every Kid's Guide to Handling Feelings.
    Chicago: Childrens Press, 1986.
Berry, Marilyn. Help is on the Way for: Thinking Skills.
    Chicago: Childrens Press, 1986.
Burns, Marilyn. The Book of Think or How to Solve a Problem Twice Your Size.
    Boston: Little Brown, 1976.
Cobb, Vicki. How to REALLY Fool Yourself: Illusions for All Your Senses.
    New York: J.B. Lippincott, 1981.
Demi. Find Demi's Dinosaurs: An Animal Game Book.
    New York: Grosset and Dunlap, 1989.
Demi. Find Demi's Sea Creatures: An Animal Game Book.
    New York: Putnam and Grosset, 1991.
Handford, Martin. Where's Waldo?
    Boston: Little, Brown, 1987.
Madgwick, Wendy. Animaze! A Collection of Amazing Nature Mazes.
    New York: Alfred A. Knopf, 1992.
Nozaki, Akihiro and Anno Mitsumasa. Anno's Hat Tricks.
    New York: Philomel Books, 1985.